PEARSON   ALWAYS LEARNING

Ronald J. Harshbarger • Lisa S. Yocco

College Algebra in Context

with Applications for the Managerial, Life, and Social Sciences

Georgia State University

3rd Custom Edition

Taken from:
*College Algebra in Context: with Applications for the Managerial,
Life, and Social Sciences*, Fourth Edition
by Ronald J. Harshbarger and Lisa S. Yocco

D1157459

Cover Art: Courtesy of EyeWire, Digital Vision, Rubberball Productions, Blend Images and Photodisc/Getty Images.
Taken from:

College Algebra in Context: with Applications for the Managerial, Life, and Social Sciences, Fourth Edition
by Ronald J. Harshbarger and Lisa S. Yocco
Copyright © 2013, 2010, 2007 by Pearson Education, Inc.
Boston, Massachusetts 02116

Pearson Learning Solutions, 501 Boylston Street, Suite 900, Boston, MA 02116
A Pearson Education Company
www.pearsoned.com

Printed in the United States of America

1 2 3 4 5 6 7 8 9 10 V092 16 15 14 13

000200010271789684

RH

ISBN 10: 1-269-44637-1
ISBN 13: 978-1-269-44637-2

Contents

Chapter 1 ▸ Functions, Graphs, and Models; Linear Functions   1

Chapter 2 ▸ Linear Models, Equations, and Inequalities   84

Chapter 4 ▶ Additional Topics with Functions   240

Algebra Toolbox 241
Linear Functions ▪ Quadratic Functions ▪ Piecewise-Defined Functions
▪ Power Functions ▪ Special Power Functions

4.1 Transformations of Graphs and Symmetry 247
Shifts of Graphs of Functions ▪ Stretching and Compressing
Graphs ▪ Reflections of Graphs ▪ Symmetry; Even and Odd Functions

4.2 Combining Functions; Composite Functions 263
Operations with Functions ▪ Average Cost ▪ Composition of Functions

4.3 One-to-One and Inverse Functions 276
Inverse Functions ▪ One-to-One Functions ▪ Inverse Functions on Limited Domains

4.4 Additional Equations and Inequalities 287
Radical Equations; Equations Involving Rational Powers ▪ Equations Containing
Rational Powers ▪ Quadratic Inequalities ▪ Algebraic Solution of Quadratic
Inequalities ▪ Graphical Solution of Quadratic Inequalities ▪ Power
Inequalities ▪ Inequalities Involving Absolute Values

Chapter 5 ▶ Exponential and Logarithmic Functions   308

Algebra Toolbox 309
Additional Properties of Exponents ▪ Real Number Exponents ▪ Scientific
Notation

5.1 Exponential Functions 312
Exponential Functions ▪ Transformations of Graphs of Exponential
Functions ▪ Exponential Growth Models ▪ Exponential Decay Models
▪ The Number e

5.2 Logarithmic Functions; Properties of Logarithms 324
Logarithmic Functions ▪ Common Logarithms ▪ Natural
Logarithms ▪ Logarithmic Properties ▪ Richter Scale